Kratom The Super Plant

Cure For Stress, Anxiety, Depression, and Addiction

By J.P. Edwin

Table of Contents

Introduction 1

Chapter I: What is Kratom?...................................... 2
    History.. 2
    Current Use 3
    Toxicity and Safety 4
    Precautions 5
    Legality... 6
    Different Kratom Types................................ 7

Chapter II: Benefits of Kratom 17
    Helps with Opioid Addiction 17
    Eases Anxiety 18
    Promotes Healthy Sleep 20
    Eliminates Stress 22
    Boosts Immune System 24
    Pain Relief 26
    Enhanced Focus 27
    Increased Sex Drive................................... 29
    Diabetes Prevention 30

Chapter III: How to Dose Kratom 32
    Beginner's Guide to Taking Kratom 32
    Tips... 33

Chapter IV: How to Take Kratom 35
    Getting the Most out of your Kratom Experience 36

Conclusion.. 37

Introduction

Kratom (*Mitragyna speciosa*) is a tropical evergreen tree that belongs to the coffee family. The kratom leaves' extracts have traditionally been used throughout the centuries as sedatives, cures or to prevent various diseases, and even stimulants – depending on the strain.

Kratom has been reported as a treatment for digestive ailments and chronic pain. More importantly, many use kratom to help overcome opioid addiction, and it is also beneficial for psychological conditions like depression and anxiety. A lot of individuals are even using kratom to help deal with erectile dysfunction.

You can't just order any strain of kratom for whatever ails you as each of them has a specific purpose. For example, you need the Kali strain with a red vein color if you need a sedative. You need one strain to help treat or prevent diabetes. You need another strain to help you deal with stress and depression.

This book will help you choose the right strain of kratom for your individual purpose. You'll know the different strains and where they're sourced. You'll also know kratom's health benefits as well as the locations where it's legal to grow and use them.

This book also discusses the ways of ingesting kratom and how to correctly dose it according to your purpose. Read up and get to know how kratom can benefit your health.

Chapter I: What is Kratom?

You may not have heard of this herb, but kratom (*Mitragyna speciosa*) is one of the most potent medicinal plants out there. Kratom is a tropical evergreen native in Southeast Asia's marshy jungles. The plant grows freely in southern and central Thailand, Myanmar, Indonesia, and other areas in the Pacific Rim.

Reaching up to 13 meters (42 feet) high, kratom has various uses in traditional medicine. The broad leaves are usually hand-plucked and then dried under the sun. The dried kratom can be brewed as a tea or pounded into powder form and taken with water.

Despite the herb having been used for medicinal purposes for the past few centuries, it is only in the current century that kratom has become known for its benefits in in other parts of the worldwide aside from Southeast Asia. Users see kratom as an aid for physical and mental development. Other users enjoy kratom for its recreational value as a sedative or as a stimulant.

While kratom is known for its medicinal purposes, the herb contains psychoactive properties and there's a slight chance for users to abuse it. Because of the herb's psychoactive properties, some countries (including Thailand) have declared kratom as a controlled substance.

History

Traditionally, kratom leaves have been used to soothe fever, numb pains and aches, manage diabetes, treat diarrhea, and alleviate addiction. The leaves have also been used as poultices on wounds or placed over the abdomen to drive away intestinal worms.

One of the more popular traditional uses of kratom is that the leaves are chewed on for energy, much like the manner coca is used in the Andes communities. On the fields, Thai workers have chewed leaves throughout the day to keep their energy levels up.

In 19th century Malaysia, kratom was used as a sedative. Instead of opium, people used kratom for its relaxing properties. Around 1921, kratom's active alkaloid mitragynine was isolated. In 1932, it was tested on humans. The effects observed were similar to cocaine.

By the 1940s, kratom was used increasingly in Thailand to manage opium withdrawal symptoms. However, kratom was banned in Thailand beginning August 1943 with the passage of the Kratom Act. This forbade everyone to cultivate the herb. All specimens were also ordered destroyed.

However, interest in kratom grew in other parts of the world. In the 1960s, other alkaloids were isolated. In 1994, 7-hydroxymitragynine was identified. In 1995, mitragynine was first synthesized.

In the early 2000s, the public became aware of kratom and its health benefits. However, the plant was already banned in Australia by 2005. In the United States, however, there are some states that consider kratom legal while other states have opted to ban the herb.

Current Use

Even if the U.S. Drug Enforcement Agency had threatened to restrict the use of kratom, interest in the herb has only spiked. On a survey covering 6,150 users, 14%

use it for anxiety, 51% use it for pain, and 9% use it for opiate withdrawal.

The herb is usually sourced from 'legal high' vendors and their products can be bought online. Of course, you won't find this product on Amazon.com.

Despite the social stigma and criminalization of its use, kratom still is popular in Thailand where the herb is used in cocktails. The '4x100' concoction is a blend of Coca-Cola, kratom tea, cough syrup, and another drug that's antidepressant, analgesic, or anxiolytic.

Toxicity and Safety

The more known indole alkaloids of kratom are 7-hydroxymitragynine and mitragynine (9-methoxy-corynantheidine). Even at high doses, mitragynine isn't toxic. In a certain study, there were no fatalities among rats given kratom doses of 1000 mg/kg. Rhesus monkeys injected with mitragynine also resulted in zero fatalities.

However, it doesn't mean that kratom is entirely safe. Various preparations may contain adulterants and phytochemicals. There's also insufficient research into regular kratom use's longer-term health risks.

From 2005 to 2011, there have been reports of a surge in seizures in Thailand. While such seizures are more attributed to the drug combinations rather than the kratom in such combinations, it still is a cause for concern.

After 8 weeks of taking kratom, liver issues may arise. Symptoms can include jaundice, abdominal pain, dark urine, itching, and/or nausea. People who take kratom incessantly may notice a darkening of the cheeks because of melanocytes' over-stimulation.

Some effects linked to heavy kratom use – although rare – include hypotension, sleep problems, tremors, sweating, temporary erectile dysfunction dry mouth, anorexia, and/or hair loss.

Certain research also suggests that psychosis (hallucinations, paranoid delusions, and confusion) can be caused by kratom use lasting for at least a decade. Studies on animals also focus on a link between excessive kratom use and learning/memory problems.

There are some human fatalities linked to kratom use, but other substances were usually present. Thus, it's difficult to pin the blame on kratom. In a certain instance, mitragynine was found together with benzodiazepines and cold medicines (over-the-counter).

Precautions

While a dose of 3 to 6 grams of kratom is the norm, any dosage above 5 grams is already considered too strong. Thus, consume kratom with water or fruit juice to counter the herb's strong taste.

There are some users who get thirsty as they start to take kratom. Thus, have a lot of water ready. Any resulting nausea can be tolerated by keeping still or lying until the nausea passes.

While it's helpful to gradually consume kratom, it may be tempting to finish the entire dose in one go so as not to experience kratom's bitter taste. If you're new to kratom, start slow using small, exact doses.

If you're an experienced user trying out a new strain, it's also important to measure the dose because of the variability among the different strains. Certain kratom products may also have adulterants like fentanyl, hydrocodone, and morphine.

Despite the benefits kratom offers, there's still a slight risk for addiction. Set a personal limit of taking kratom just once or twice weekly so you will not develop a dependency to it. Addiction symptoms can include weight loss, anorexia, frequent urination, insomnia, darkened skin, and constipation.

Lasting for about one week, kratom withdrawal symptoms can include muscle pain, weakness, cravings, lethargy, jerkiness, nausea, insomnia, diarrhea, and hallucinations.

Legality

Many users take kratom to manage anxiety, pain, and/or other conditions. However, others also consider kratom to be a 'plant teacher' – a tool for growth and exploration. Kratom can draw attention gently to areas of interpersonal and personal dysfunction. There are also a number of users who report that the herb improved their sexual performance and reduce anxiety.

Despite the popularity of kratom, there's also the question of its legality. While not controlled federally in the United States, kratom is still a 'drug of concern.' States like Tennessee, Indiana, Vermont, Wisconsin, Alabama, and Arkansas have banned kratom. There are also other states with pending legislation concerning kratom.

In the United Kingdom, kratom is banned under the Psychoactive Substances Act. In New Zealand, kratom is regulated and those who intend to use it need a prescription to acquire it. The herb's active alkaloids are controlled by various measures in European Union member states like Poland, Sweden, and Denmark. Kratom is also illegal in Australia, Myanmar, Malaysia, and Thailand.

Despite kratom being banned in certain parts of the world, including countries that it's native to, there are still a lot of users who find the plant to be more beneficial than disadvantageous. The following chapters document the various kratom strains and types and what they're good for. Also to be discussed are the proper kratom dosages for particular conditions.

Different Kratom Types

There are various kratom strains, although kratom is classified generally into three colors: red vein, green vein, or white vein. The classification is dependent on the stem and leaf vein's color.

If you closely look at a kratom leaf, you will notice that the vein and the stem have a particular color. This determines the kratom leaf's effects on the body and the mind.

The colors mean a specific effect and a different chemical composition. The vein and the stem are removed during grinding. Essentially, only the leaf part is taken.

Red Kratom

Red kratom has veins and stems that are colored red. The red variety is the most widely available and best-selling strain on the market, with the red vein variety sold more than the white and green vein combined.

Red kratom abundantly grows in Southeast Asia and is slightly hardier than many other Mitragyna Speciosa trees. There are studies that suggest the veins' red color enables the plant to be susceptible less to external factors.

Generally, red vein kratom strains offer peace of mind as well as optimism and a feeling of wellbeing. This variety is also used as a sleep aid and used by those suffering from insomnia. The red strains are also known to relieve pain and relax the body.

Red vein kratom can replace or supplement pharmaceutical painkillers. The strongest red kratom extracts are used to prevent opiate addicts' withdrawal symptoms.

Even among the red vein strains, there are marked differences in properties and effects. Strains like Red Vein Borneo and Red Thai have sedative properties while other strains like Red Sumatra offer an elated mood. In small doses, the red vein produces a stimulating effect. However, the red veins are used to promote tranquility and peace.

White Kratom

White vein kratom is a stimulant. The effect of each white kratom strain depends on factors like the product's quality and the individual's tolerance level. White kratom strains are also the most euphoric and stimulating strains.

Instead of coffee (caffeine), people are gradually taking white kratom for concentration, cheerfulness, and alertness. White kratom is also used for increased stamina, motivation, and concentration during long work hours.

People who may feel exhausted or experience gloomy moods are benefited when they use white kratom. However, you should not take this when you're about to go to sleep. To achieve a well-balanced energy boost, mix white kratom with red vein strains.

Green Kratom

Green vein kratom's effects are a mix of the white and the red strains. It also provides mild energy-boosting effects.

Individuals use it to get in the 'flow,' making them experience better focus and alertness. The green strains are subtler than the white or red strains. Green kratom is used generally to treat pain and other discomforts. Green kratom also does not cause drowsiness, which is a characteristic side effect when a person takes analgesic supplements.

To create a more sophisticated effect and to come up with a more rounded flavor, green kratom can be used with white or red kratom strains. When mixed properly, green kratom prevents red veins' excessive anesthetic effects and white veins' overstimulation effects.

Green kratom may also be used to boost confidence. You may disregard other people's opinions and impressions and you will feel less afraid. Thus, green kratom is popular for recreational activities, an example of which is a night out in town. You become cheerful, friendlier, and more talkative.

Red, White, and Green Strains

A lot of people unfamiliar with kratom may have questions about each strain's various effects. Below are some of the more popular kratom strains.

Bali

Bali kratom is one of the most popular kratom strains in the market. This is because of its optimum blend of properties and higher potency. For years, the Bali kratom strain was one of the few strains available.

Bali kratom is a red variety, but unlike other reds that have sedative properties, the Bali kratom gives a mild energy boost. This strain, however, does have the pain relief properties offered by red varieties.

Bali can also aid in relaxation and brings a mild euphoric state. This strain's dosage is ½ to 3 teaspoons.

Maeng Da

Considered the most potent raw leaf strain, Maeng Da kratom is also known as 'Pimp's Kratom.' This strain has been used historically for various purposes. Many users find Maeng Da energizing, yet it offers a sense of relaxation.

The Maeng Da strain was created by grafting different plant tissues are joined together to integrate each plant's qualities into a new strain.

Maeng Da was created to come up with a strain that relieves pain yet mitigates sedative effects so it may not affect a user during work hours. This kratom strain was created as a strong red kratom strain amid the humidity and heat of Indonesia.

Like the Bali strain, Maeng Da boosts energy and offers pain relief. However, to beat the Indonesian heat, Maeng Da was blended to offer a more potent energy kick than Bali.

As it's bred especially for its alkaloid properties, Maeng Da still offers a red strain's conventional pain relief properties yet integrates an energy boost that other red kratom strains lack. This strain's dosage is ½ to 3 teaspoons.

Super Green Malaysian

Super Green Malaysian is known for its energizing, potent aroma. Grown in the Malaysian forests, Super Green Malaysian is a sought-after kratom strain. It's popular because of its potency due to the high alkaloid concentration in Malay kratom leaves.

The Super Green Malaysian strain has some of any kratom strain's longest lasting effects. One gets a smooth experience from the high alkaloid concentration, which leads to an energy boost without the user losing concentration. This strain's dosage is ½ to 3 teaspoons.

Red Kali

Also known as the 'original kratom,' the Red Kali (Red Kalimantan) strain is a pure kratom variety from Southeast

Asia's Borneo region. While its purity makes it somewhat less potent than other strains, Red Kali still offers the conventional kratom qualities that many still look for.

As a traditional red kratom, the milder Red Kali strain offers long-lasting relaxation and pain relief. This strain's dosage is ½ to 3 teaspoons.

Green Vein Kali

The Green Vein Kali kratom strain comes from Kalimantan in Borneo Island, Indonesia. This particular strain has a comprehensive kratom effect spectrum, which is typical of the strain's high mitragynine content.

The combination of Green Vein Kali's alkaloids leads to milder yet longer lasting effects than other kratom varieties. While some kratom strains are more potent when it comes to relaxation and pain relief effects, and others provide more energy, Green Vein Kali has a combination of qualities. This strain's dosage is ½ to 3 teaspoons.

White Vein Kali

The White Vein Kali kratom strain comes from Kalimantan in Borneo Island, Indonesia. This strain has an uplifting, stimulating aroma.

With an alkaloid mix that diminishes – yet doesn't eliminate – some of its pain relief and sedative alkaloids, the White Vein Kali strain may be more energizing than Red Vein Kali. However, the former still has certain pain relief qualities.

Certain white strains provide a potent energy boost, which may overwhelm some individuals. However, the White Vein Kali strain has some of a red strain's sedation and pain relief properties that helps balance out the white strain's high energy kick.

While the White Vein Kali is a mild white kratom strain, one can still get a decent surge of energy. This strain's dosage is ½ to 3 teaspoons.

Red Indo

Red Indo is a classic Indonesian kratom strain with an aroma that's typical of kratom trees with red leaves. Red Indo's relaxing and sedative effects are milder than the effects of Red Kali, thus, making Red Indo is more energizing.

The Red Indo strain is slow-burning and long-lasting. While this kratom strain doesn't have the Red Kali's potency, it still has potent pain relieving properties with milder sedative effects. This strain's dosage is ½ to 3 teaspoons.

Green Indo

The Green Indo strain is a classic Indonesian kratom strain with a characteristic green leaf aroma. This strain can be blended with the Red Indo strain.

While the concentration of alkaloids may not be as high as that of Super Green Malay, Green Indo's alkaloid combination leads to milder yet longer lasting effects than other strains. This strain's dosage is ½ to 3 teaspoons.

White Vein Indo

The White Vein Indo kratom strain contains the full spectrum of kratom alkaloids. Some users notice a marked stimulating, euphoria-inducing aroma.

This rare strain is highly sought for its dissociative and long-lasting pain relief properties. The purest forms of this strain are grown from the Indonesian jungles. This strain also offers mild, energy-boosting effects. This strain's dosage is ½ to 3 teaspoons.

White Vein Thai

The White Vein Thai kratom strain is popular for its uplifting, stimulating characteristics. This strain complements well with the White Vein Indo strain.

The White Vein Thai strain shares potent energizing effects with other Thai strains and other white vein strains. The blend of alkaloids increases euphoria and energy.

However, this strain still has some pain relief properties. This strain's dosage is ½ to 3 teaspoons.

Ultra-Enhanced Indo Extract

The Ultra-Enhanced Indo Extract strain is made from deveined Indo kratom's pure alkaloids, and is then integrated with the Bali strain. This strain is standardized by weight at 17% alkaloids.

Ultra-Enhanced Indo Extract brings out specific kratom attributes yet brings out various effects like relaxation, pain relief, and a mild mood and energy boost.

Despite its similarity to the Bali strain in terms of effects, the Ultra-Enhanced Indo Extract has more potent pain relief properties. This strain's dosage is about 1 gram. It's even less if mixed with powdered kratom leaf.

Gold Reserve Kratom Extract

The Gold Reserve strain is a highly respected kratom strain, and is potent in amounts of ½ to 1 gram. Gold Reserve is a classic kratom reformulation that mixes highly concentrated alkaloids with natural kratom leaf.

Gold Reserve is similar to the Bali strain in that they're both well-rounded and their effects are potent. Gold Reserve brings together a blend of pain relief, stimulation, an energy boost, and full body relaxation.

The Gold Reserve strain is more stimulating than coffee, and it does not come with the 2 o'clock crash and the jitters. This strain's dosage is 1 gram. It's even less if mixed with powdered kratom lea

Natural Enhanced True Thai
The Natural Enhanced True Thai strain doesn't contain synthetic chemicals, only a blend of natural green vein kratom leaf and 90% pure kratom alkaloids. The alkaloids are from a True Thai strain that's rare.

Natural Enhanced True Thai is a more potent version of conventional Thai kratom strains. It offers mild energy-boosting properties as well as significant relaxation/pain relief effects. This strain's dosage is 0.25ml or more.

ISOL-8 Extract
The ISOL-8 Extract strain has a minimum of 8% mitragynine and a full spectrum of other kratom alkaloids that are naturally extracted. This strain has energy stimulating effects similar to caffeine.

The ISOL-8 strain provides kratom's stimulating and energizing effects, and gives you the boost that you normally derive from constant coffee consumption. This strain's dosage is 1 gram. It's even less if mixed with powdered kratom leaf.

Natural Enhanced White Sumatra
The Natural Enhanced White Sumatra kratom strain is a combination of 90% pure kratom alkaloids and all-natural white vein kratom. The strain is derived with alkaloids from a special Sumatran white kratom strain.

Natural Enhanced White Sumatra is a reformulation that results from a potent white vein kratom strain. This strain is preferred by individuals wanting white kratom's effects with an extra kick.

Natural Enhanced White Sumatra provides an energy boost with powerful relaxation and pain relief effects. This strain's dosage is 1 gram. It's even less if mixed with powdered kratom leaf.

Red Hulu Kapuas

The leaves of the Red Hulu Kapuas strain have a high 7-hydroxy mitragynine content that makes the strain a good analgesic. Red Hulu is better for stress management than the green and white Kapuas strains.

However, the red strain is not recommended as a nootropic, of which property is better attributed to the white and green Kapuas strains.

The Hulu Kapuas strains are rare and they grow freely in the Hulu forest, which is an Indonesian forest near Borneo. The Hulu forest is located on the Kapuas river banks.

The Kapuas River is close to the Malaysian border, and is not near a populated area. This means only kratom dealers are likely to access the site.

Green Hulu Kapuas

The leaves of the Green Hulu Kapuas strain are non-stimulating and non-sedative. They are used to achieve moderate effects than the red and white leaves. The Green Hulu Kapuas strain offers only mild potency.

White Hulu Kapuas

The leaves of the White Hulu Kapuas strain have only minimal 7-Hydroxy Mitragynine content, yet the leaves contain other alkaloids in abundance. The white leaves are used to treat depression, stress, and panic attacks. White Hulu Kapuas also provides energy.

The white Kapuas strain is also an excellent nootropic, and is best if used early in the morning. However, this strain is not so efficient when it comes to pain relief.

Red, White, or Green?

The kratom strain that's appropriate for your purpose depends on your situation and on your personal preference. This can be a complicated matter with kratom as the effects can vary within the same color of strain. It depends on location, quality, harvesting method, and climate, among others. Red vein kratom strains vary among one another, as do green and white veins.

A good way for you to determine the kratom type that suits you is to order a sample kratom pack. The pack has kratom powders of all the kratom strains. When you order a sample pack, you can determine easily which kratom strain is right for you.

Chapter II: Benefits of Kratom

Kratom leaves have been used traditionally for medicinal purposes. Kratom leaves' interesting health benefits include their ability to boost metabolism, relieve pain, improve immunity, increase sexual energy, and prevent diabetes. Kratom also helps with addiction, eases anxiety, induces healthy sleep, and eliminates stress.

While kratom can be beneficial for the health, withdrawal from it can lead to certain side effects. These include weight loss, anorexia, insomnia, muscle pain and spasms, aching in the bones and muscles, jerky limb movement, hot flushes, watery nose/eyes, decreased appetite, fever, and diarrhea. Psychological symptoms normally include restlessness, nervousness, anger, tension, aggression, hostility, and sadness.

Helps with Opioid Addiction

There's anecdotal evidence that kratom can help in opioid addiction therapy, with kratom ingestion reducing opioid withdrawal symptoms. Kratom's effects include sedation, euphoria, anxiety relief, and pain relief, making kratom potentially useful for addiction treatment.

Since kratom activates similar receptors as opioids, it can diminish the withdrawal symptoms that result when a person stops using opioids. The kratom activates another class of opioid receptors than prescription opioids or heroin, allowing kratom to decrease the symptoms of withdrawal without causing the same highs as conventional opioids do.

While there's substantial evidence that points toward kratom as an effective opioid addiction treatment tool, there has yet to be any clinical or experimental studies that truly assess kratom's scientific validity in the treatment of opioid addiction.

Kratom works well in effectively dampening and alleviating dangerous drugs' adverse effects. It also aids in easing the after-conditions of opioids when attempting to overcome and combat them to get back to sobriety.

Suggested Strains.

Some of the recommended strains to help deal with substance and opioid addiction include Borneo, Bali, Maeng Da, and – depending on certain conditions – Indo kratom strains. The ideal kratom leaf vein color is red, and the prescribed dosage is moderate to high.

While there are those who have tried and believe that kratom can help deal with opioid addiction, there are others who are skeptical of kratom's addictive properties. Psychoactive substances, of which kratom is an example, carry an addiction risk.

There are a number of people who actually got addicted to kratom after a period of daily use, which is why it is important to be careful when using it to self-treat opioid addiction.

Moreover, there are serious side-effects linked to excessive kratom use including paranoia, hallucinations, and liver damage and hypothyroidism in certain cases. Since kratom is sold as an herbal supplement, it does not entail government oversight as prescription drugs do.

Eases Anxiety

Kratom leaves are used widely as anxiolytic substances for individuals who suffer from chronic depression, stress, mood swings, and anxiety. By regulating bodily hormones, people can get relief from chemical imbalance symptoms without having to depend on pharmaceuticals and the side effects derived from those drugs.

The use of kratom for anxiety relief can be tricky if you are not experienced with such method to treat worry, nervousness, apprehension, and concern. If you need to treat anxiety, you just can't go for the first kratom item you see on the market.

The many kinds of kratom strains have different various effects. If you choose the wrong strain, especially a kratom strain that provides energy, it will provide little benefit especially if you want to relieve nervousness and anxiety.

When used for its intended purposes, kratom in the relief of anxiety is non-addictive and is safe for consumption. While benzodiazepines are the common anxiety treatments, they can be addictive.

Kratom extracts work as sedatives that can calm nerves and release muscle tension. Beverages made with kratom – like tea – help the body by helping the mind relax. Some of kratom's benefits in anxiety relief include:

Reduced panic attacks

Elevated energy levels

Positive feeling

Muscle relaxation

Normal sleeping habits

Kratom helps in the binding of opioid receptors, and it contains two alkaloids: 7-hydroxymitragynine and mitragynine. These alkaloids unite brain receptors.

When you ingest a low dose of kratom, alkaloids bind the brain receptors with the delta opioids. In high dosages, alkaloids bind the receptors with the mu-opioid. Opioids are substances naturally produced by the body for pain relief.

After taking the kratom that's appropriate for anxiety relief, you experience a euphoric sensation.

As compared to conventional pharmaceuticals, kratom has fewer side effects. Kratom alkaloids result in more stimulation and reduced addiction when taking lower doses. The effects of vigor and motivation derived from kratom and potent and efficient to reduce anxiety.

Suggested Strains.

Some of the effective strains to be used in the relief of anxiety include Borneo, Indo, and Bali. The Borneo strain has more finely-potent alkaloids to overcome anxiety and restlessness. The ideal color vein for use is the red strain while the prescribed dose is moderate.

However, if you want anxiety relief, stay away from the Maeng Da and Thai Kratom strains. Maeng Da can be confusing for beginners as there are energy-boosting varieties and anti-anxiety varieties. Deciding on the right variety takes trial and error.

If you're not sure about the varieties, just avoid the Maeng Da strain. On the other hand, the Thai Kratom strain can boost energy and may worsen anxiety because of its stimulant effect.

Promotes Healthy Sleep

Kratom is mostly known for its sedative effects. For a long time now, people have been using kratom to relieve pain and assist in opiate withdrawal. However, another usually overlooked benefit of kratom is its ability to battle insomnia and promote better sleep.

Not only is insomnia an inconvenience to its sufferers, the condition can also lead to adverse effects like energy loss, moodiness, subpar physical performance, lesser function, and the inability to deal with stressful events.

Suggested Strains.

The best strain to provide insomnia relief is the Red Vein Kratom. This strain is proven effective in sedation and helps in correcting sleep issues because of its soothing, calming effects. Some of the best variations of this strain include Red Vein Bali Kratom, Red Vein Sumatra Kratom, and Red Vein Borneo Kratom.

When it comes to treating insomnia, use Borneo, Sumatra, or Bali kratom. You need to be careful and responsible of your kratom intake to rule out any possible side effects. Don't take the same kratom strain every night. Consume kratom strains alternately to avoid tolerance to a certain strain and to keep the dosage low.

How does red vein kratom help with insomnia? This strain contains naturally formed alkaloids essential to maintain a healthy body and mind interaction. The alkaloids 'communicate' with the receptors of the body. The receptors then signal the brain for positive reactions like physical ease, sedation, and stress relief.

Physical Ease.

Kratom is rich in Hydroxymitragynine, an alkaloid that aids in the promotion of physical comfort. Many users say the feeling is like being wrapped in a blanket, helping to induce sound sleep as well as to provide comfort.

Sedation.

Because of its sedative effects, kratom can help a person deal with insomnia. Through sedation, a person feels more relaxed and doesn't feel much pain. This allows the person to sleep better and fall asleep quickly.

Stress Relief
. Insomnia may be a result of anxiety and stress. As such, kratom can help battle insomnia due to its anxiolytic and anti-stress properties. With the consumption of kratom, a person may once again have a regular sleep pattern and vastly reduced stress levels.

Even non-insomniacs can benefit from the use of kratom. They can take a relaxing strain of kratom in low doses.

Kratom Safety for Insomnia
There are some users who report that taking kratom before going to bed helps to give them a sense of security and have a good night's sleep. These users don't report any 'kratom hangover', but they feel refreshed instead and feel a clear mind while waking up.

Eliminates Stress
If you are prone to stress and tend to suffer from depression or anxiety, kratom can help calm you down and soothe your nerves. As a psychostimulant, kratom releases serotonin and endorphins that enhance your overall mood.

Kratom calms your mind so you won't experience anxious thoughts. Kratom's calming effect eases tension that helps greatly with social anxiety, making you feel more sociable and confident. This is the reason why some native tribes in Southeast Asia take kratom during social gatherings.

People today face constant stress or pressure, be it from work or from other issues. A lot of people are loaded with various commitments that can be overpowering. Stress can affect everyone.

Stress can affect the body and can add to a range of medical issues like heart disease, strokes, skin disease, skin issues, hypertension, anxiety, and depression. Aside from dealing with stress, taking kratom in the right doses helps relieve other conditions like heart palpitations, anxiety, hyperventilation, sweating, and muscle cramps, among others.

Kratom soothes and calms down the inner triggers that can cause the mind to spiral through depressive and anxious thoughts. To successfully manage stress, detrimental and negative thoughts must be reframed or dispensed with into a more positive or joyous circumstance.

Thus, kratom is useful for people suffering from mood swings, chronic stress, depression, anxiety, PTSD, panic attacks, and those with highly stressful jobs.

The right strain of kratom can give you a relaxing feeling. However, the effect depends on the dosage and type. Certain kratom strains are stronger than others. When taken in high quantities, kratom gives off a euphoric sensation.

Suggested Strains.

The Borneo kratom strain is used traditionally to reduce stress and insomnia. The strain is also being used to treat opiate withdrawal and chronic pain. If you suffer from anxiety and stress, the green vein can benefit you the most.

A lot of anxiety sufferers found the Borneo green vein strain to be as effective as benzodiazepines (or other prescription sedatives) without the side effects. Borneo kratom has potent concentrations of the 7-hydroxymitragynine alkaloid, making it one of the most sedating kratom strains.

Another popular strain for people to help deal with stress is the Bali kratom. The red vein strain of Bali kratom is great for pain relief and comes with potent sedating qualities. The green and red varieties are greatly believed to reduce anxiety and stress.

Because of its sedative effect, the Bali kratom strain is not ideal if you want to increase energy. While the green and red strains have sedative properties, the white strain is different as it provides a mild energy boost while still giving off a relaxing feeling.

Malay strains are also used in stress management. Malay strains offer stress and anxiety relief, but it does not make you drowsy. Thus, the Malay variety is normally used by social anxiety sufferers.

The Red Vein Malaysian strain has more sedating and pain relief effects than green vein. This strain enhances mood and promotes relaxation, which means it's good for stress relief, anxiety, and pain.

Boosts Immune System

Independent studies on the various kratom leaves' alkaloids determined that the combative effects can greatly affect the immune system's resilience and strength. Traditionally utilized as herbs, kratom leaf extracts have antimicrobial and free radical scavenging abilities, and is also an excellent antioxidant source.

The body's immune system is important for long-term and overall health. Consisting of numerous components including organs, tissues, and cells, the immune system is the body's main line of defense against infections and germs. When triggered, the immune system responds by eliminating harmful foreign substances from the body's internal systems.

Poor health can be the case when the immune system is sluggish to react. The immune system may also overreact, mistaking healthy or normal substances as foreign invaders. Such situations interfere the overall wellness.

If you feel you're about to go down with a cold, kratom can help by giving your immune system a boost so your ailment will not push through. When it comes to prevention, regularly take a micro dose of kratom to keep your immunity in excellent shape.

How does kratom help boost immunity?

It is kratom's alkaloids that provide the therapeutic effects, especially when it comes to protecting the immune system. Some kratom alkaloids that have immuno-stimulant properties include:

Isorhynchopylline – mainly an immuno-stimulant.

Isopteropodine – mainly an immuno-stimulant.

Isomitraphylline – may also be an anti-leukemic agent.

Mitraphylline – non-narcotic, diuretic, and anti-hypertensive. It's also a muscle relaxant.

For centuries, people have been using kratom as a medicinal herb. Kratom is said to improve immunity for disorders like flu, the common cold, and even serious medical conditions like cancer. People have thus adopted a habit of taking this herb with illness' onset to drastically reduce intensity and duration.

Kratom is a potent antioxidant, and it has been discovered to reduce neurological damage when an individual is suffering a stroke. Kratom's alkaloids can also help reduce high blood pressure. Moreover, kratom has anti-bacterial and anti-viral properties that can help boost immunity.

Suggested Strains.

Some of the suggested strains to boost the immune system include the Malay and Borneo strains, the ideal vein color to strengthen the immune system is green, and the ideal dosage is low to moderate.

Pain Relief

Kratom leaves have potent analgesic properties that helps quickly relieve pain. Kratom does this by affecting the hormonal system. The amount of dopamine and serotonin released increases when kratom leaves are chewed.

The kratom alkaloids essentially dull pain receptors all over the body. Moreover, you get the pain relief qualities of opiates or morphine, but without risking addiction.

Those with osteoarthritis, osteoporosis, osteomalacia, rheumatoid arthritis, chronic backache, and joint pain can benefit from kratom's pain relief properties.

Kratom's pain relief properties are also effective for chronic pain, as compared with other herbs used for medicinal purposes.

A lot of individuals have radically changed the way they took painkiller medicines as they have started to shift to using herbal treatments like kratom.

With the growing awareness of kratom's beneficial attributes, it is likely that kratom be used as an alternative to conventional synthetic pain relief pharmaceuticals in the future.

Kratom can effectively diminish pain from conditions like:

Backache
Intensive migraine or headache
Multiple sclerosis

Minor injuries (including broken bones, burns, and scrapes)

Damaged muscles

Scoliosis

Neck strain or soreness

Abdominal soreness

Chest pain

There are also other areas wherein kratom can successfully soothe and mitigate pain.

Kratom's two most powerful alkaloids – Mitragynine and 7-OH Mitragynine – especially enhance the herb's ability to significantly alleviate pain. These two alkaloids contain active opioid delta receptors that mitigate the body's pain sensitivity. Therefore, it's crucial to use specific Kratom leaf strains that contain the optimum levels of the two vital alkaloids.

Suggested Strains.

As the potency of alkaloids within the leaves' content varies among the various kratom strains, certain strains have been tested to be most effective in pain management.

The recommended strains for pain relief include Borneo, Indonesian (Indo), Maeng Da, and Bali. The ideal vein color is red and the suggested dosage is moderate to high.

Enhanced Focus

When you take kratom, you can have sharper concentration and more focus, which should make your tasks seem much easier. Kratom's stimulant effects may also make you feel more motivated and inspired to face any kind of challenge.

Other users report a euphoric feeling and a clearer state of mind. You would feel less worried, more relaxed, and more optimistic. Others have reported increased sexual desire and performance.

Aside from improving and enhancing focus, kratom can also stimulate creativity, which is great if you are faced with brain-intensive tasks.

How does kratom enhance focus? Kratom unleashes a person's productivity. By acting on the brain and periphery's opiate receptors, kratom's alkaloids (mitragynine and 7-hydroxy mitragynine) help you work longer and harder, with more focus than usual. Moreover, acetycholine's release calms down the mind, allowing you to better focus.

Additionally, the release of serotonin and dopamine, which are feel-good chemicals, further increase attention span, motivation, and focus for the task in front of you. Thus, you can focus on your work and provide more quality results.

As a natural herb, kratom is without synthetic side effects that can adversely and permanently affect neurological effectiveness. Kratom improves the overall level of memory, focus, and intelligence by eliminating the psychological 'noise' in the background while raising overall concentration level.

Through natural methods, kratom helps in enhancing memory, adjusting core attention, and vitalizing alertness.

Suggested Strains.

Some of the suggested strains for enhancing focus are the Malay, Maeng Da, and Thai kratom. The Malay strain in particular is used to enhance intelligence, focus, and memory.

The Maeng Da strain is used for improvement of intelligence, focus, memory, and vigor. The Thai strain is used for improvement of intelligence focus, memory, and vigor.

The ideal kratom vein colors for enhanced focus are green and white, and the prescribed dose is from low to moderate.

Increased Sex Drive

Kratom is considered by users and traditional practitioners as a fertility booster and as an aphrodisiac. The extra blood flow and extra energy brought on by the consumption of kratom can help reenergize a slow libido, increase fertility, and improve conception/duration rates.

Seeking a balance between sexual performance and kratom usage can be delicate and is more related to the kratom strain and the dosage. In the traditional context, kratom can enhance sexual function. This makes sense as kratom is a natural stimulant used to improve physical performance.

Sex drive and basic tactile stimulation can be especially enhanced during the stimulation phase. Kratom's sedation and analgesic effects lessen sex organs' sensitivity, and require a bit more time and stimulation to achieve an orgasm. This is useful for men who have troubles with premature ejaculation.

While kratom possesses muscle relaxing properties (to improve erections) and functions as a mild vasodilator, its use as a sex drive enhancer is related to the ingested amount.

Kratom, when taken in large amounts, can negatively impact sexual performance, and can lead to temporary erectile function issues. An overdose of kratom can reduce overall libido, sexual drive, and libido in the same manner as any opiate or opioid would.

A heavy relaxing and calming experience is physically pleasant and can lead a user's mind to drift away from sex's physical aspect and venture towards the spiritual. The combination of sex and kratom can be beneficial when taken in stimulating and lower doses.

When taken sparingly, the user will immediately notice an upshift in his mood. The person also feels more adventurous, interactive, and outgoing, all of which can help sexual experiences' sensation.

Suggested Strains. Users suggest the Green Hulu Kapuas for enhanced sexual performance. You may also enhance the effect with yohimbine, which is an herb that increases kratom's effects.

The green or white vein kratom strains have less concentrations of 7-hydroxy mitragynine alkaloids. Such strains are therefore recommended to boost libido. There are also users that suggest the Bali strain. The dosage is 1 gram, which is enough to keep libido up for about 12 hours.

Don't use the red strains, especially Red Vein, as they contain high amounts of 7-hydroxy mitragynine alkaloid, which can cause sexual dysfunction.

Diabetes Prevention

While kratom is best known to promote better sleep, reduce stress and anxiety, or even promote better sexual performance, it's also used to promote better physical health – particularly in the treatment of diabetes. Kratom leaves can positively affect blood sugar levels.

Limited research indicates that the leaves' alkaloids can help regulate glucose and insulin in the blood, effectively preventing the potentially dangerous troughs and peaks of energy that diabetics experience periodically. Kratom not only helps diabetics manage their condition, kratom also helps prevent diabetes from occurring in the first place.

There is no exact science as to how kratom works to treat diabetes except that the herb has two properties – relaxation and pain relief – that can help manage the condition.

Kratom can help prevent diabetes as it also helps to bring down blood pressure.

Kratom's pain relief benefits is also use to manage diabetes' painful side effects. Kratom's analgesic and stimulating properties can help diabetics suffering from peripheral neuropathy.

Suggested Strains. The more effective strains that can help prevent and manage diabetes are the red and the white strains. However, there are certain green strains that can also help manage diabetes symptoms. The red strains help lower high blood pressure and the white strains help in the management of chronic pain.

Other strains that can help with diabetes management include Green Malay, Maeng Da, and White Maeng Da. Red strains help lower high blood pressure while the white strains help relieve pain.

In many instances, the most effective dosage in the prevention and treatment of diabetes is by adopting the 'trial-and-error' method. It also depends on the strains consumed and the reason for taking kratom.

Chapter III: How to Dose Kratom

When using kratom for its medicinal properties, take the right strain and right dose to achieve the desired effects. If you take a lower-than-needed dose, you may not feel anything at all, but if you use a higher dose than recommended, you will feel some discomfort, like nausea and dizziness. Conversely, if the dose is higher-than-needed, you may be feeling temporary side effects like 'wobbles' or slight nausea.

Take the dosage in optimum amounts so that kratom's real purpose is fulfilled efficiently and effectively.

Dosage for Focus and Energy. Take 3 to 6 grams daily, with results varying from person to person. To improve the dose's efficacy, mix kratom with grapefruit juice.

Dosage for Pain and Anxiety. Take 7 to 9 grams to produce positive results. Begin taking smaller doses before taking higher doses. If you rush into taking more, you may experience and inconvenient sedating effect, which can be counterproductive during the day.

Opiate Withdrawal Dose. To withdraw from opiates, start with 7 to 9 grams of kratom powder. Take the powder for at least 2 to 4 times daily for about 3 days. On day 4, reduce the dose to 5 to 7 grams. On day 5, reduce more to 3 to 5 grams. On day 6, you should be taking only 2 grams kratom. On day 7, stop taking the kratom powder.

Beginner's Guide to Taking Kratom

Below is a general guide to know the right dose for a certain strain. Do this for each new strain you try. When you take kratom, make sure you take it early in the morning or about 2 to 3 hours after consuming food.

On an empty stomach, take 2-3 grams. After 20 minutes, you should start to feel its effects. If not, you may still start to feel a certain sensation.

Assess how your body feels after 30 to 45 minutes. Take 1 to 2 grams more if you feel you need a higher dose.

After taking the extra dose, assess how your body feels after 15 to 30 minutes. By this time, you should feel a particular sensation and you will find out if the kratom strain is effective or not.

If you think you need a bit more kratom, raise the dosage by 0.5 to 2 grams.

At such point, you should be feeling something positive. From there, just go about your day for the next 4 to 5 hours.

After the time has passed and you feel you need to take more kratom, repeat the process with the same strain utilized earlier in the day.

Since you're a beginner to taking kratom, 3 to 5 grams may be sufficient. If you're below 150 pounds in weight, you may even start out with just 1.5 grams.

Tips

Here are several things that you may want to keep in mind before you take kratom.

Kratom on an empty stomach. When starting out with kratom or when using a new strain, it's best to take kratom when your stomach is still without food. You may experiment with taking the herb even when you have eaten, but do this when you have taken kratom for a period of time. A partially-full or full stomach requires a higher dose of kratom.

Drink water. Kratom can dehydrate you, so you should drink a lot of water when taking it. If you feel a bit light-headed when taking kratom, the dose you just took may be higher than normal and you need a lot of water to wash it down.

Keep a log. Take notes every time you try out a new kratom strain. Note its effects, when you took it, how much you took, and many others. Take note of your feeling and thoughts when ingesting a particular kratom strain. The notes will help you build on your kratom-taking experience.

Chapter IV: How to Take Kratom

Kratom, which comes in powder or pill/capsule form, is usually ingested. Here are a few ways to consume the herb.

Tea. For about 30 minutes, you boil the kratom powder. Allow to sit for a few minutes and then strain the liquid off. While many people think the effects of the tea are better and more consistent, the process is more time consuming.

If you're patient, this method of taking kratom may be appropriate for you. The tea's taste isn't bad and you can drink it cold or hot. The tea tastes better chilled though.

Toss n'Wash. Measure out the kratom dose into a glass. Tip the powder gently into your mouth, swill the kratom and then swallow. You can split the dose into several mouthfuls so you don't throw up the powder.

Add to Yogurt. You can add kratom powder to yogurt, which is what some people do. Add the kratom to a fruit-flavored yogurt as the goal is to mask the kratom powder's taste.

In Capsule Form. If you don't want to taste the kratom, taking it in capsule form is quite convenient. However, a drawback to this is that you need to take several capsules to get a sufficient dose. Make sure to take the kratom capsules with plenty of water.

Protein Shake. This method works, that is, if you don't mind the extra calories that come with the shake. You also have to taste the kratom longer. However, some people claim kratom's positive effects are felt more when it's taken in smoothie form.

Getting the Most out of your Kratom Experience

When you regularly use kratom, your body develops an immunity to kratom. If you regularly take the same strain, the receptors of your brain will adapt. Kratom's effectiveness can weaken and you'll be needing more doses. By using alternate strains, however, you'll keep your brain's receptors fresh and maintain kratom's potent effect.

This is crucial if you're taking the herb for pain-relief purposes as the analgesic effects may be reduced over time otherwise. Rotating kratom strains ensures you get the potent euphoric, energizing, and medicinal effects of the herb.

Your kratom experience may vary. To get optimal results from taking kratom, experiment with various vein types and strains, and document your results. If a certain strain doesn't work, try another one until you find the best strain for your purpose. This way, you'll determine what vein colors and strains are best for you.

Conclusion

Despite kratom possessing numerous health benefits, its psychoactive effects make it illegal in some states in the United States as well as in some countries.

There are reports that kratom, which has little to no risk of overdose risk, can help people stop taking opiates. Moreover, kratom can help reduce the dependence on potentially harmful prescription painkillers. There are experts who say that kratom can be used in place of methadone, Vivitrol, and buprenorphine to treat opioid addiction.

A few million people use kratom to positive results, based on retailer reports. However, many states ban it. While the United States doesn't have current federal regulations on the sale or possession of kratom, there are still states that prohibit the substance's use.

Some of the states that have totally or partially banned the use of kratom include Alabama, Arkansas, California (San Diego only), Florida (Sarasota County only), Indiana, Tennessee, and Wisconsin. In Illinois, you need an ID to buy kratom if you're in Jerseyville. In New Hampshire, you can buy kratom once you reach the age of 18.

While kratom is grown in Malaysia, Myanmar, and Thailand, the herb's use is banned in these countries. Kratom is also banned in Australia. In Germany, kratom can be used for medicinal purposes.

In New Zealand, one needs a prescription to get kratom leaves. However, it's legal to grow, buy, or sell kratom in Ireland, Italy, Canada, and the United Kingdom.

With so many gray areas, what is the future of kratom use? Kratom, a powder or pill that's known to deliver super-human strength, feelings of euphoria, enhanced focus, and potent pain relief, is yet to be legalized. There is limited available research on the plant, and the existing research on its negative effects is largely based on reports that involve other drugs.

Other animal research has been conducted and have shown that the use of kratom can lead to addiction. However, surveys on users indicate that withdrawal symptoms from kratom are no worse than those encountered when quitting other herbal supplements or coffee.

The U.S. Drug Enforcement Agency has recently stated that it would classify kratom as a Schedule I drug, making it illegal and placing it on the same level as marijuana, LSD, and heroin. The public outrage, however, has led the DEA to postpone the proposal.

Kratom users are nevertheless unfazed about the DEA's stance on the herb, and a lot of sellers says such controversy has only boosted business. Many people are now interested to try out this lesser-known herb with few disadvantages and numerous benefits.

There's still a lot of ambiguity concerning kratom, with others saying kratom can negatively affect health despite the majority of users lauding the herb's capabilities. However, if people are quick to prematurely judge kratom as harmful to the health, they may only harm the other individuals who can benefit from kratom's positive aspects.